This book
belongs to

_____

_____

_____

for RD

This edition published 2015.
First published in Australia in 2012 by Lex & Lucy Publications.
Illustrations copyright © Kathryn Wendy Deighton, 2012.
Text copyright © Eleni Prineas, 2012.

The rights of Kathryn Wendy Deighton and Eleni Prineas to be
identified as the illustrator and author of this work have been
asserted.

Published in Australia by Lex & Lucy Publications
lexandlucy@gmail.com
ISBN 978 0 9873976 2 1

My 2 Mums & Me

Kath Deighton

Eleni Prineas

Lex & Lucy

Mummy and Memmy
are at the zoo

I am too
Peek-a-boo!

Mummy and Memmy
are playing in the dirt

I am too
See my shirt!

Mummy and Memmy
are making a drink

I am too
See, mine's pink

Mummy and Memmy
are making bread

I am too
See, mine's red

Mummy and Memmy
are cleaning the room

I am too
See my broom

Mummy and Memmy
are playing the drums

I am too
See my tum!

Mummy and Memmy
are trying to draw

I can draw
on the floor!

Mummy and Memmy
are in the sea

I am too
right up to my knee!

Mummy and Memmy
are switching off the light

I am too
Good night, sleep tight

If you enjoyed this book, look out for number 2 in the series:

Ballet & Me

by Kath Deighton & Eleni Prineas

Lightning Source UK Ltd.
Milton Keynes UK
UKRC02n2128011217
313720UK00003B/5